W9-CRE-649

ORIGO
STEPPING STONES 2.0
COMPREHENSIVE MATHEMATICS

AUTHORS

James Burnett

Rosemary Irons

Peter Stowasser

Allan Turton

PROGRAM CONSULTANTS

Diana Lambdin

Frank Lester, Jr.

Kit Norris

STUDENT JOURNAL

ORIGO
EDUCATION

INTRODUCTION

ORIGO STEPPING STONES 2.0

The *ORIGO Stepping Stones 2.0* program has been developed to provide a balanced approach to teach and learn mathematics. It has been developed by a team of experts to create a world-class comprehensive math program. Each kindergarten student has two books.

THE STUDENT JOURNAL

The Student Journal consists of 12 modules with 6 lessons in each. Some lessons have more than one journal page. Here are the key features of the pages.

PERFORATED PAGES

Young students need many hands-on experiences to sort, match, compare, and order quantities, pictures, words, and numerals long before they can write. The perforation in this journal allows students to remove and cut out images for use in activities such as these.

Space for the student's name when a page is removed.

MODULE AND LESSON

This shows Page B of Lesson 5 in Module 1.

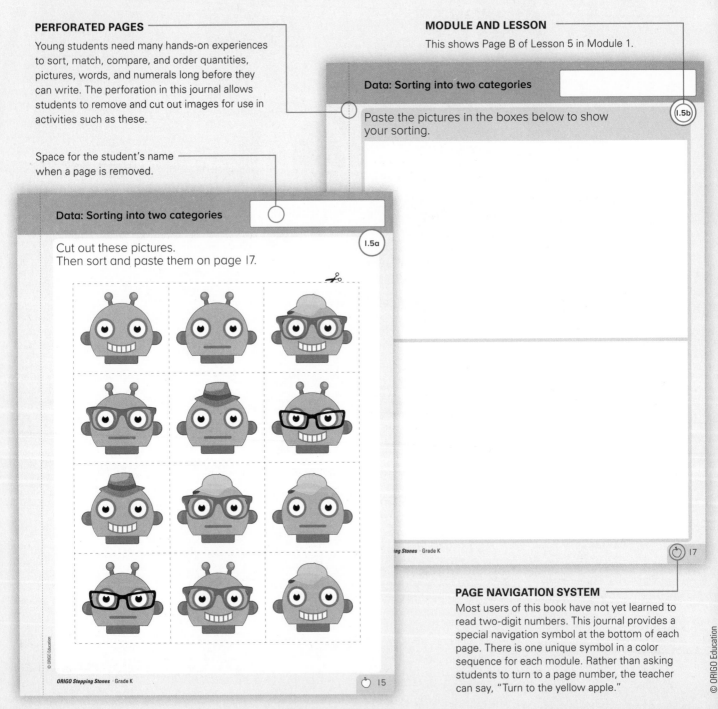

Data: Sorting into two categories

Paste the pictures in the boxes below to show your sorting.

1.5b

Data: Sorting into two categories

Cut out these pictures.
Then sort and paste them on page 17.

1.5a

ORIGO Stepping Stones · Grade K

15

© ORIGO Education

ing Stones · Grade K

17

PAGE NAVIGATION SYSTEM

Most users of this book have not yet learned to read two-digit numbers. This journal provides a special navigation symbol at the bottom of each page. There is one unique symbol in a color sequence for each module. Rather than asking students to turn to a page number, the teacher can say, "Turn to the yellow apple."

© ORIGO Education

INTRODUCTION

THE PRACTICE BOOK

Regular and meaningful practice is a hallmark of *ORIGO Stepping Stones 2.0*.
Each module in this book has pages that provide practice of content from
the previous Student Journal module, and pages that practice numeral
writing or computation.

MODULE AND LESSON

PERFORATED PAGES

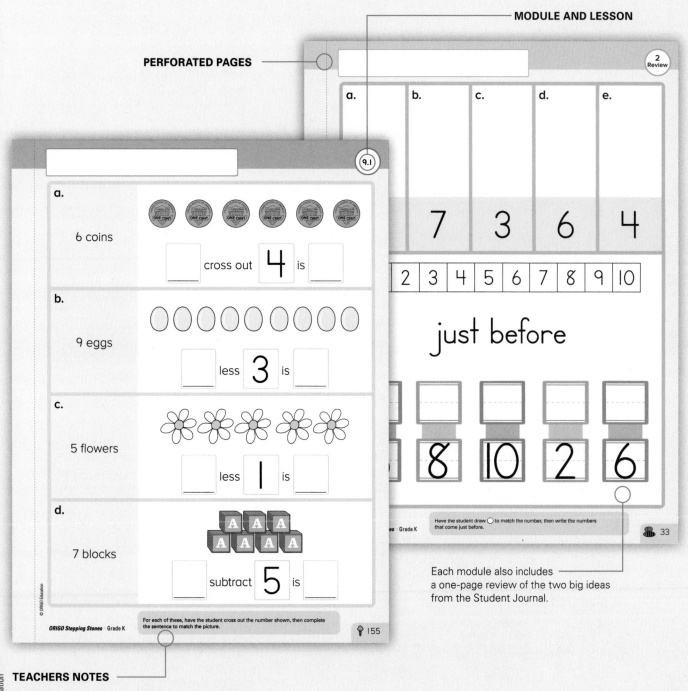

Each module also includes a one-page review of the two big ideas from the Student Journal.

TEACHERS NOTES

Brief notes reduce instructions for students to read.

© ORIGO Education

CONTENTS

© ORIGO Education

CONTENTS

© ORIGO Education

1.1b

Paste the cats in the picture below to show different groups.

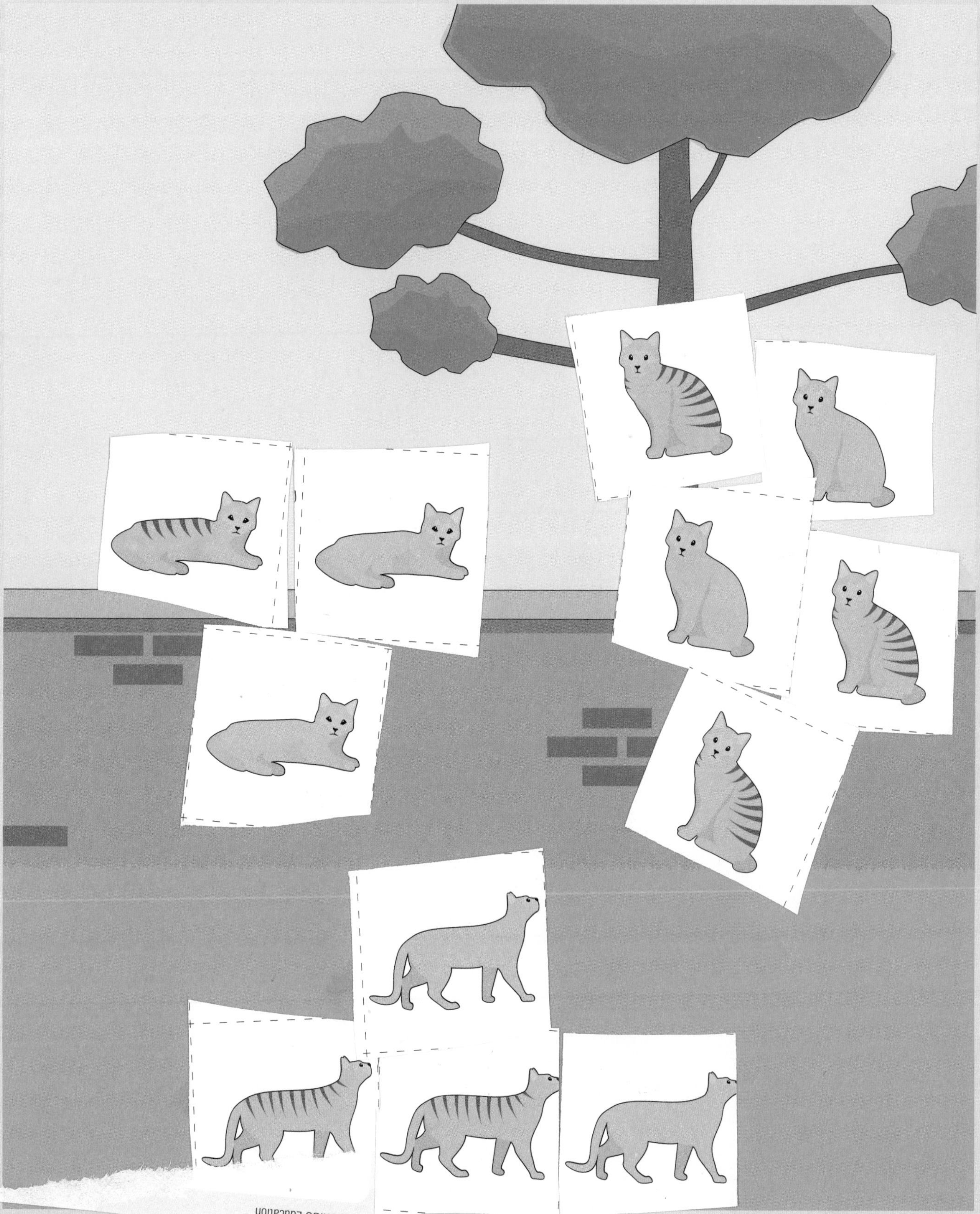

© ORIGO Education

Place a pocket on the shirt. Then place the matching number of counters on the shirt.

1.2b

What are counters?

© ORIGO Education

Paste the matching number of fingerprint faces.

a.

4

b.

2

c.

3

d.

5

e.

1

© ORIGO Education

Number: Working with 1 to 5

Color balls to match each numeral.

1.4

a.

4

b.

2

c.

1

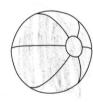

d.

5

e.

3

© ORIGO Education

Data: Making yes/no graphs

Paste faces on the graph to show **yes** or **no**.

Have you been on an airplane?

yes	no

How do we use the other faces?

© ORIGO Education

Paste cards in the boxes.
Then circle the **greater** number in each pair.

3.3b

a.

1   ⑥

b.

2   ⑦

c.

③   8

d.

④   ⑨

e.

⑤   ⑩

© ORIGO Education

Length: Making comparisons

Color the pictures blue that are **shorter** than your string.
Color the pictures yellow that are **longer** than your string.

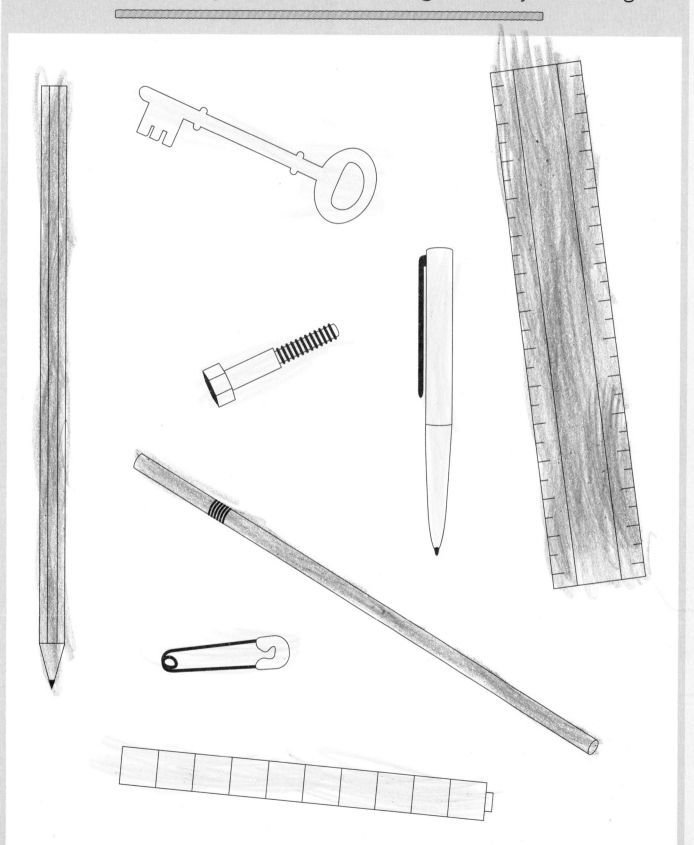

© ORIGO Education

Mass: Making comparisons

Circle the toy that is **lighter**.

a.

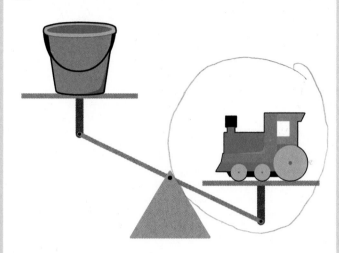

b.

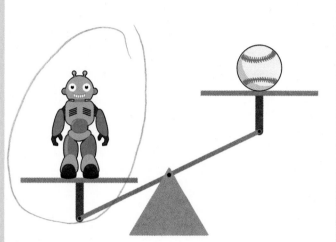

c.

d.

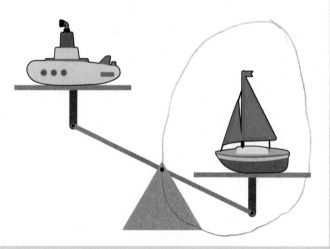

e.

f.

© ORIGO Education

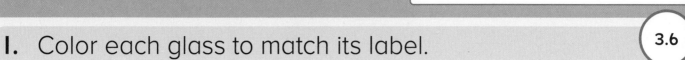

1. Color each glass to match its label.

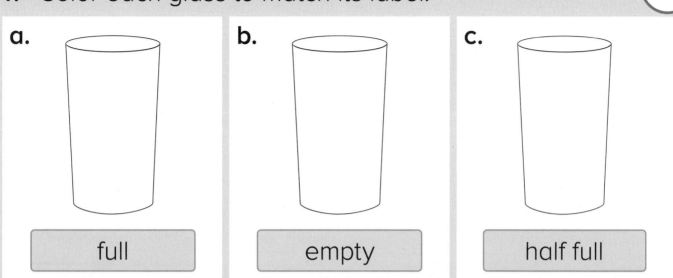

a.

full

b.

empty

c.

half full

2. Circle the glass that is holding **more** water.

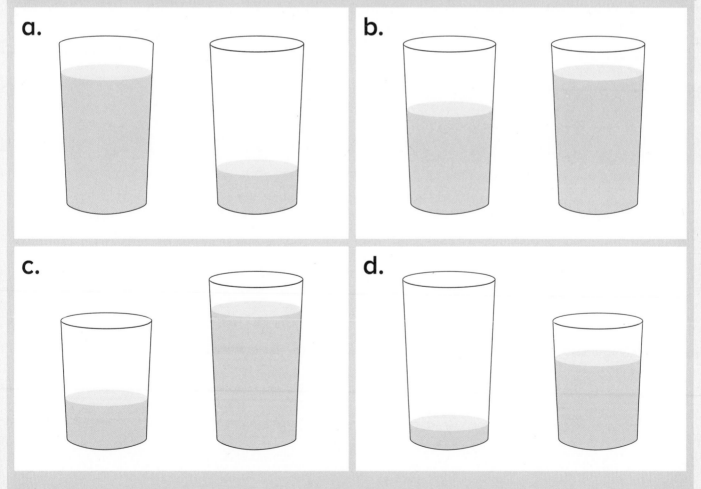

a.

b.

c.

d.

3. Look at **all** the glasses in Question 2. Write **L** on the glass that is holding the **least** amount of water.

© ORIGO Education

Write each number name.
Then draw the matching number of ◯.

4.1

a.
10 ten   ten

b.
7 seven   seven

c.
6 six   six

d.
3 three   three

e.
0 zero   zero

Number: Writing number names (5, 9, 4, 8, 2, 1)

Write each number name.
Then draw the matching number of ◯.

4.2

a. 5 five — five
b. 9 nine — nine
c. 4 four — four
d. 8 eight — eight
e. 2 two — two
f. 1 one — one

ORIGO Stepping Stones · Grade K

Paste the numeral and number name on the matching quantity.

a.

b.

c.

d.

e.

f.

g.

h.

i.

j.

k.

© ORIGO Education

1. Draw the number of ○ to match each numeral.

4.4

a.
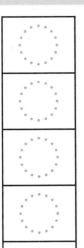

b.
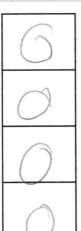

c.
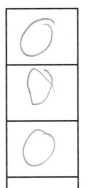

6   5   8

2. Write the numeral to match the number of ●.

a.
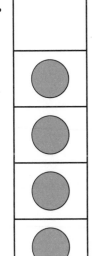

b.
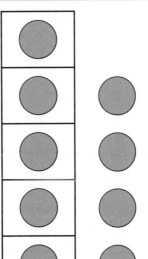

c.
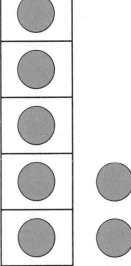

4   9   7

© ORIGO Education

1. Draw ◯ on the ten-frame to match each numeral. number

4.5

a.

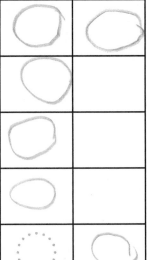

7

b.

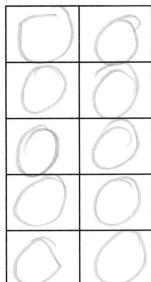

10

c.

8

2. Write the numeral to match the number of ⬤.

a.

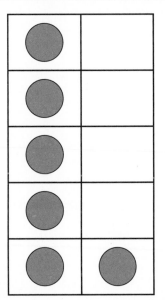

b.

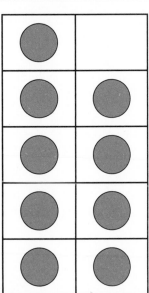

c.

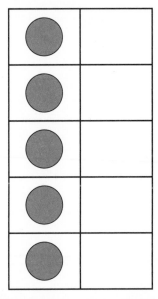

© ORIGO Education

Write the numeral to match the number of dots.

a.

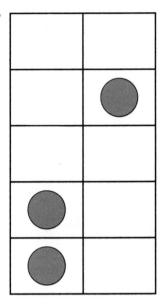

3

b.

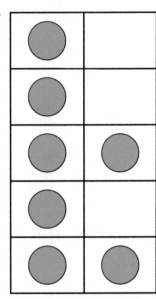

7

c.

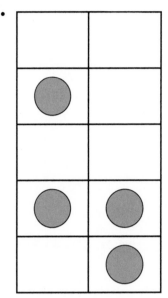

4

d.

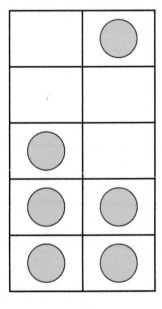

6

e.

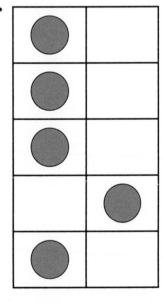

5

f.

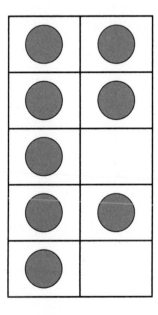

8

© ORIGO Education

Draw ○ in each empty box to make each balance picture true. Then complete the sentence to match.

5.1

a.

3 and 1 balances 4

b.

2 and [ ] balances 7

c.

2 and [ ] balances 3

d.

3 balances [ ] and 3

© ORIGO Education

Equality: Identifying an unknown part in balance situations

Draw ◯ in each empty box to make each balance picture true. Then complete the sentence to match.

5.2

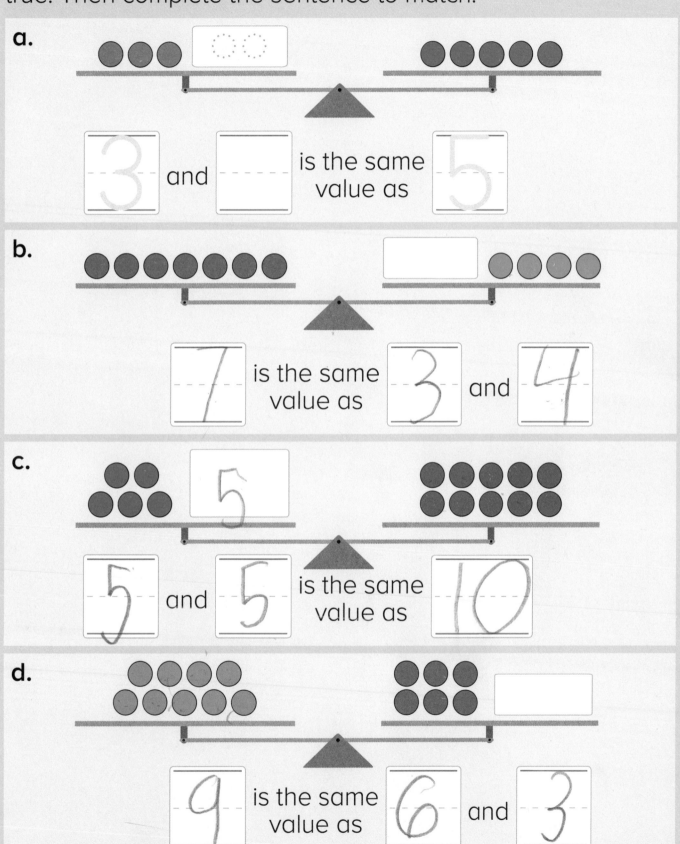

a. 3 and ___ is the same value as 5

b. 7 is the same value as 3 and 4

c. 5 and 5 is the same value as 10

d. 9 is the same value as 6 and 3

© ORIGO Education

Equality: Identifying two parts that balance a total

Draw ◯ in each empty box to make each balance picture true. Then complete the sentence to match.

a.

7 balances **6** and **1**

b.

10 is the same value as **5** and **5**

c.

6 balances **4** and **2**

d.

9 is the same value as **7** and **2**

© ORIGO Education

Equality: Developing the language of equality

Draw ◯ in each empty box to make each balance picture true. Then complete the sentence to match.

a.

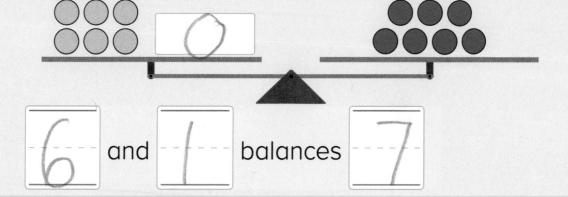

6 and 1 balances 7

b.

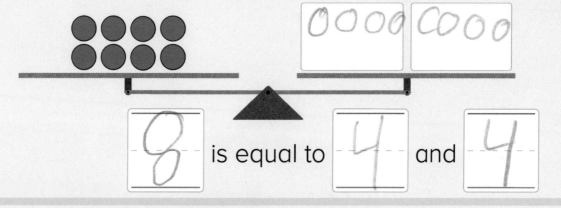

8 is equal to 4 and 4

c.

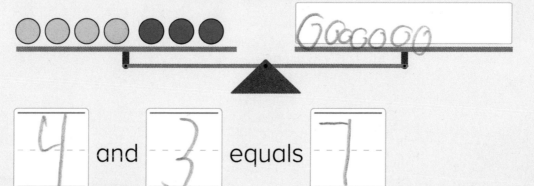

4 and 3 equals 7

d.

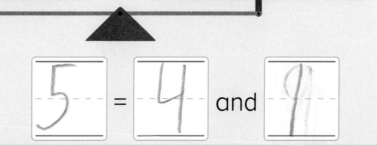

5 = 4 and 1

© ORIGO Education

Circle in red each astronaut's **right** hand and **right** foot.

5.6

© ORIGO Education

Addition: Adding two groups (put together)

Use two colors to show two groups.
Then write the number in each part and the total.

a.

 and makes 6

2 and 4 makes 6

b.

 and is

3 and 4 is 7

c.

4 plus 4 equals 8

 plus equals

d.

5 add 4 = 9

 add

© ORIGO Education

Draw a matching number of shapes.
Then trace over the number name.

a. 14 fourteen

b. 16 sixteen

c. 17 seventeen

© ORIGO Education

7.2

Draw a matching number of shapes.
Then trace over the number name.

a.

19 nineteen

b.

18 eighteen

c.

15 fifteen

© ORIGO Education

Color the matching number of shapes.
Then trace over the number name.

a.

13 thirteen

b.

12 twelve

c.

11 eleven

d.

20 twenty

© ORIGO Education

Write the number of tens and ones.

a.

_____ ten and _____ ones

b.

_____ ten and _____ ones

c.

_____ ten and _____ ones

d.

_____ ten and _____ ones

e.

_____ ten and _____ one

© ORIGO Education

Subtraction: Representing situations (take apart)

Parth

Cross out the number shown. Then complete the sentence. **8.1**

a.

8 balls

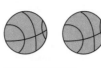

8 cross out 1 is 7

b.

6 books

6 cross out 3 is 3

c.

7 eggs

7 less 6 = 1

d.

9 balloons

9 less 4 = 5

e.

5 crayons

0 subtract 5 = 0

ORIGO Stepping Stones · Grade K

111

Subtraction: Writing equations (take apart)

Write the total. Cover 1 or 2 dots.
Then write the number of dots that are left.

a.
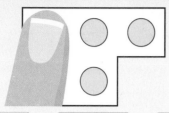

$5 - 2 = \boxed{}$

b.
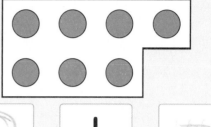

$8 - 1 = 7$

c.
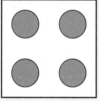

$5 - 1 = 4$

d.
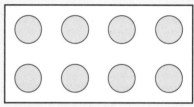

$10 - 2 = 8$

e.
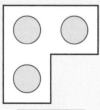

$5 - 2 = 3$

f.
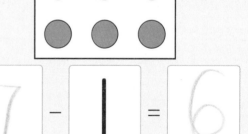

$7 - 1 = 6$

g.
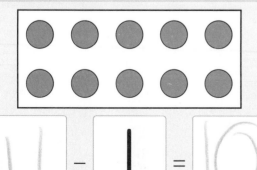

$11 - 1 = 10$

h.
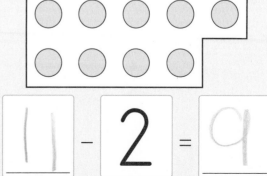

$11 - 2 = 9$

© ORIGO Education

Complete each sentence to match the picture.

8.3

a.

4 take away 1 is 3

b.

5 take away 2 is 3

c.

7 take away less 3 is equals 4

? Less and equal

d.

5 take away less 1 is equals 4

e.

9 subtract 5 = 4

© ORIGO Education

Write an equation to match each picture.

8.4

a.

7 − 2 =

b.

7 − 3 = 4

c.

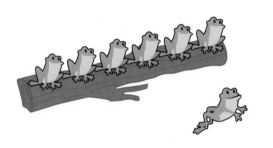

6 − 1 = 5

d.

2 − 2 = 0

e.

3 − 2 = 1

f.

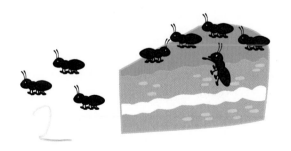

5 − 3 = 4

© ORIGO Education

Write an equation to match each picture.

a.

$$9 - 4 = 5$$

b.

$$5 - 3 = 2$$

c.

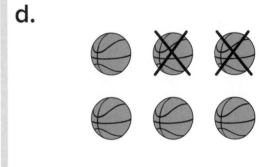

$$7 - 3 = 4$$

d.

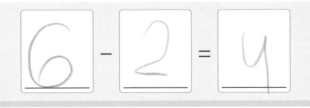

$$6 - 2 = 4$$

e.

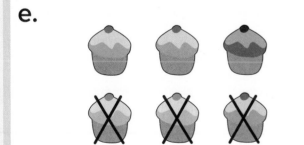

$$6 - 3 = 3$$

f.

$$8 - 3 = 5$$

© ORIGO Education

Read each clue then write a matching number.
Some clues have more than one match.

9.3

| 1 | 2 | 3 | 4 | 5 | 6 | 7 | 8 | 9 | 10 | 11 | 12 | 13 | 14 | 15 | 16 | 17 | 18 | 19 | 20 |

My number is

a. between 11 and 15

b. less than 4

c. greater than 8

d. one less than 12

e. one greater than 19

f. between 15 and 17

g. one greater than 5

h. between 16 and 20

© ORIGO Education

Number: Solving number puzzles

Read each clue then write a matching number.
Use the number track to help your thinking.

1	2	3	4	5	6	7	8	9	10	11	12	13	14	15	16	17	18	19	20

My number

a. has 1 ten and 6 ones

16

b. has 1 ten and 2 ones

12

c. is 2 greater than 7

27

d. is 3 less than 5

35

e. add 4 makes 6

10

f. add 7 makes 8

15

g. subtract 1 is 4

0

h. subtract 2 is 5

3

ORIGO Stepping Stones · Grade K

129

Addition: Decomposing numbers (up to 10)

Color some of the blocks. Then write an equation to match. **10.2**

a.

$4 + 1 = 5$

b.

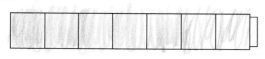

$6 + 1 = 7$

c.

$3 + 1 = 4$

d.

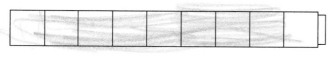

$8 + 1 = 9$

e.

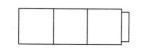

$3 + 1 = 4$

f.

$2 + 1 = 3$

g.

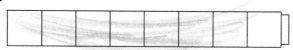

$6 + 2 = 8$

2D shapes: Identifying shapes

Sort the 2D shapes and paste them where they belong. **10.5b**

a. triangles

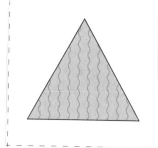

b. circles

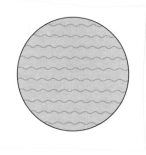

c. squares

d. non-square rectangles

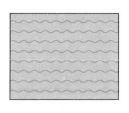

e. other shape

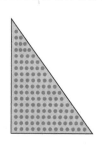 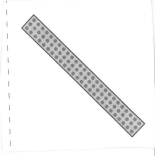

© ORIGO Education

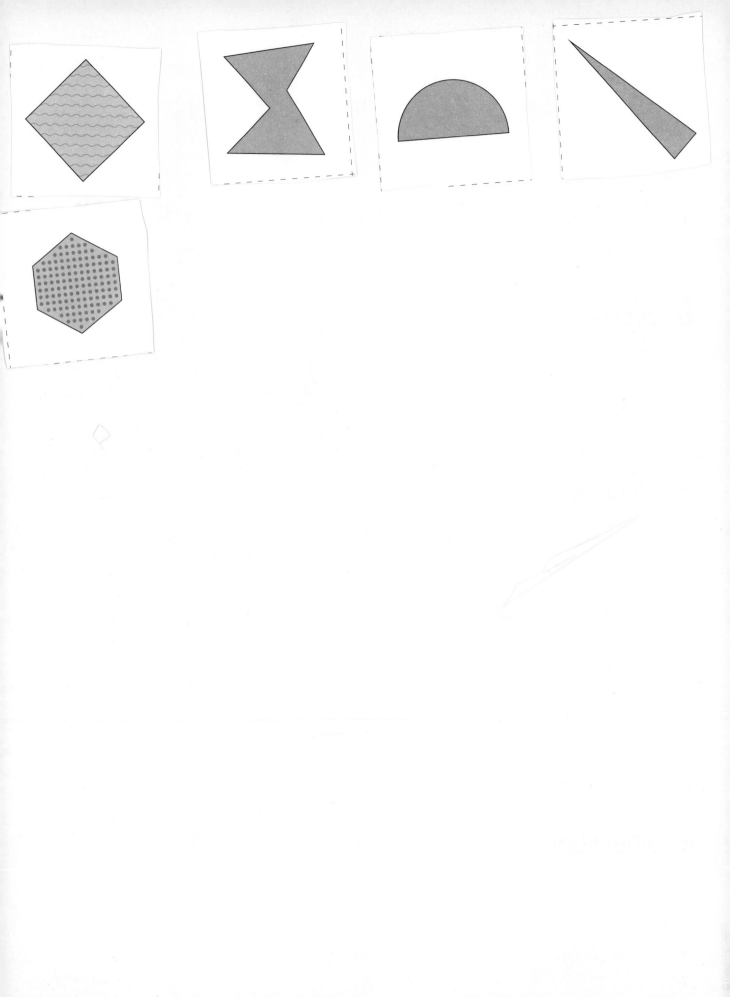

Write the number of sides and corners for each shape.

a.

 sides corners

b.

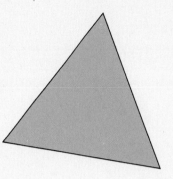

 sides corners

c.

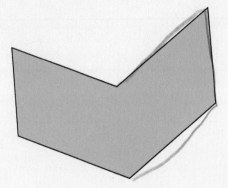

 sides corners

d.

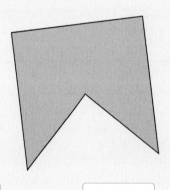

5 sides 5 corners

e.

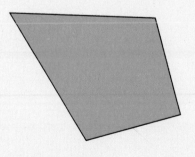

 sides corners

f.

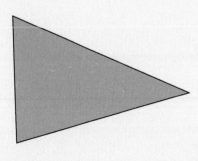

3 sides corners

© ORIGO Education

Circle **+** if you think the problem is about addition.
Circle **−** if you think the problem is about subtraction.

11.1

a. Alexis has 8 dollars.
She spends 2 dollars at the store.
How much money does she have left?

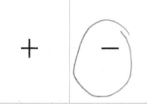

b. 9 friends are in a swimming pool.
2 friends get out.
How many friends are still in the pool?

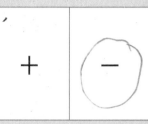

c. 4 dogs have short hair.
5 dogs have long hair.
How many dogs are there in total?

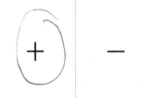

d. There are 7 pennies in the purse.
2 more pennies are dropped into the purse.
How many pennies are in the purse now?

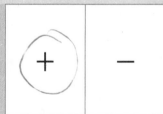

e. Felix buys 6 baseball cards.
He gives 2 cards to Zoe.
How many cards does Felix have now?

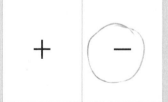

f. 8 horses are in the stable.
2 horses are in the field.
How many horses are there in total?

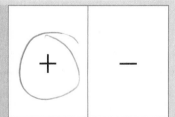

g. There are 5 muffins on the tray.
2 muffins are banana. The rest are berry.
How many muffins are berry?

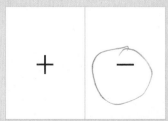

Addition/subtraction: Solving word problems (act out)

Use blocks to act out each problem.
Then write an equation to show the answer.

a. 7 birds were sitting on the fence. One bird flew away. How many birds are left?

O O O O O O O̸

$7 - 1 = 6$

b. Claire counts 3 blue cars and 3 red cars. How many cars did she count in total?

O O O+O O O

$3 + 3 = 6$

c. There are 10 players on the soccer team. 3 players are boys. The rest are girls. How many girls are on the team?

O O O O O O O O

$10 - 3 7$

d. Anoki packs 2 toys in the box. Amos packs 6 more toys in the same box. How many toys are now in the box?

O O+O O O O O O

$2 + 6 = 8$

e. Emilia has 6 strawberries and 4 blueberries. How many berries does Emilia have in total?

O O O O O O O+O O

$6 + 4 = 10$

f. 3 friends are playing on the swings. 6 more friends join them. How many friends are now playing?

O O O+O O O O O O

$3 + 6 = 9$

Draw pictures to solve each problem.
Then write an equation to show the answer.

a. There are 5 balls. 2 balls roll away. How many balls are left?

three 3

b. 4 crayons are red. 2 crayons are green.
How many crayons are there in total?

six 6

c. There are 6 eggs. One egg is broken.
How many eggs are left?

U U U U U U

five 5

d. Tyler has 3 pennies. He finds 4 more pennies.
How many pennies does he have now?

O O O O O O O

Seven 7

Addition/subtraction: Solving word problems (write equations)

Write an equation to solve each problem.

a. 5 friends are playing in the pool. 2 friends get out of the water. How many friends are left in the pool?

three 3

b. Beatrice scored 2 goals in the first game. She scored 4 goals in the next game. How many goals did she score in total?

six 6

c. Daniel has 9 baseball cards. He loses 3 cards. How many baseball cards does he now have?

six 6

d. The zoo has 4 adult tigers and 3 tiger cubs. How many tigers are there at the zoo?

Seven 7

e. There are 6 fish in the tank. 2 fish are hiding. How many fish can be seen?

four 4

f. There are 2 horses and 6 cows on a farm. How many animals are there in total?

eight 8

© ORIGO Education

Copy each picture.

a.

b.

c.

Cut out the 12 shapes and paste them on page 163.

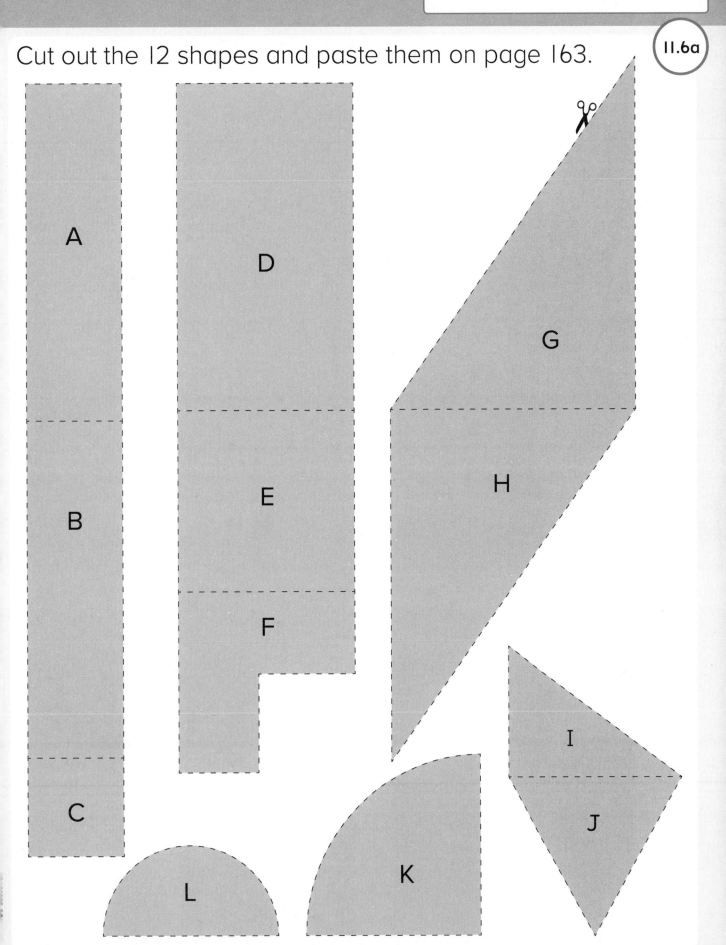

A

D

B

G

E

H

F

C

I

J

K

L

Paste two shapes together to match each outline.

I. Draw a line from each coin to its name. 12.1

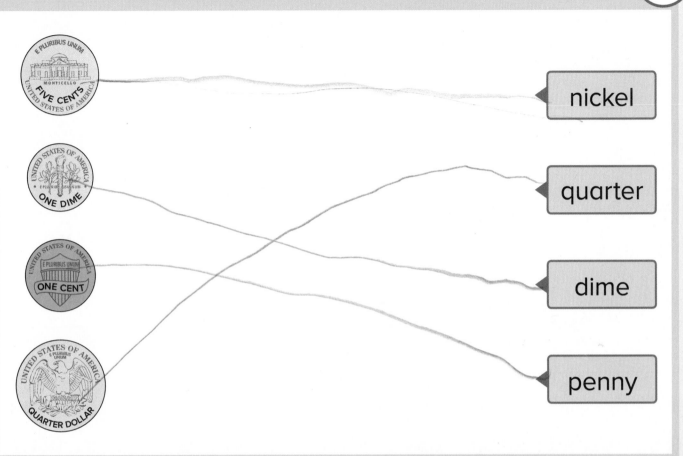

2. Think about the size of each coin. Then draw a line to match each coin outline to the coin name. Use real coins to help.

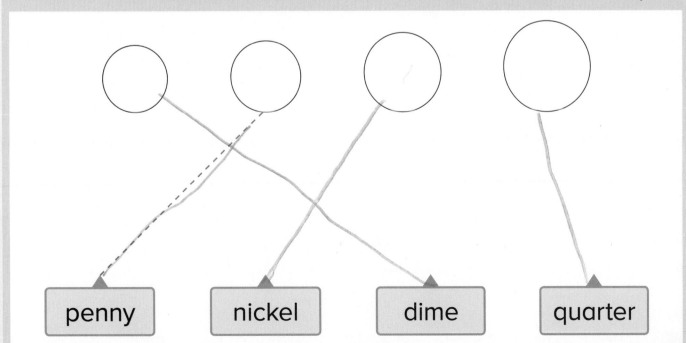

Cut out and paste the matching coins inside each purse on page 169.

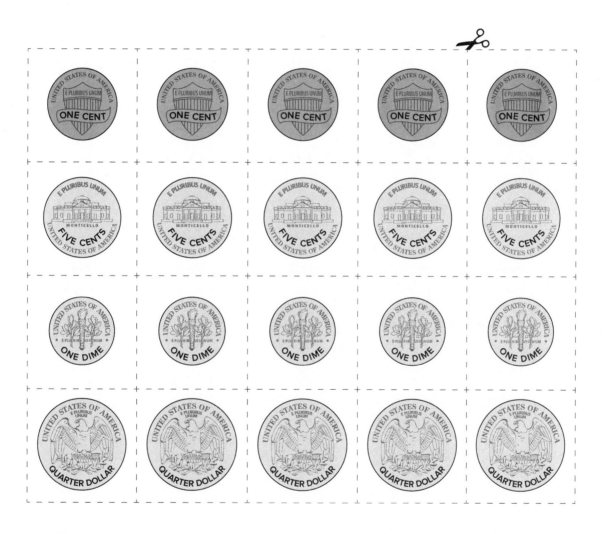

© ORIGO Education

Money: Showing groups of coins

Paste the matching coins inside each purse.

a.

3 dimes
2 pennies

b.

2 nickels
1 quarter

c.

1 penny
1 quarter
1 nickel

d.

2 quarters
1 nickel
1 dime

© ORIGO Education

Cut out and paste coins to show the amount on each price tag on page 173.

© ORIGO Education

I. Draw a line from each coin to its matching value.

12.3b

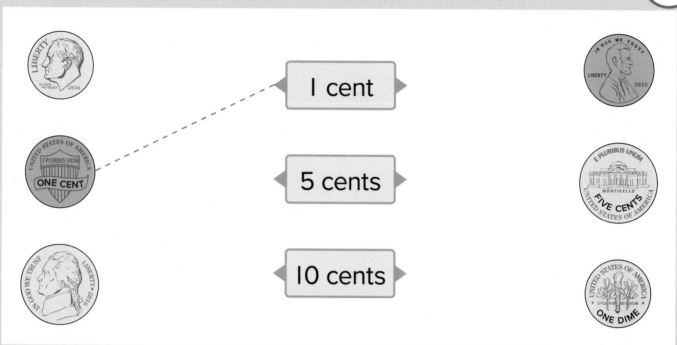

	1 cent	
	5 cents	
	10 cents	

2. Paste coins to show the amount on each price tag.

a.

3 cents

b.

II cents

c.

6 cents

© ORIGO Education

Cut out and paste coins to show the amount on each price tag on page 177.

12.4a

© ORIGO Education

Money: Working with coins

Paste coins to show the amount on each price tag.
Then show the same amount in a different way.

12.4b

a.

13 cents

b.

5 cents

c.

16 cents

© ORIGO Education

Keep the patterns going.
Then draw your own pattern that repeats.

a.

b.

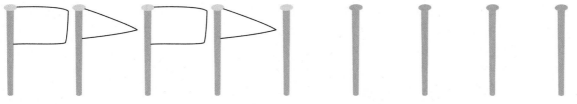

c.

d.

e.

© ORIGO Education

Talk about the pattern. Draw the missing parts.

a.

b.

c.

d.

e.

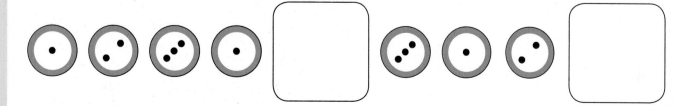

© ORIGO Education

STUDENT GLOSSARY

2D shape

A **two-dimensional (2D) shape** has straight sides, curved edges, or straight and curved edges. For example:

 triangles

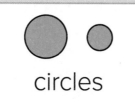 circles

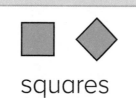 squares

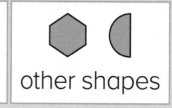 other shapes

3D object

A **three-dimensional (3D) object** has flat surfaces, curved surfaces, or flat and curved surfaces. For example:

 cone

 cylinder

 cube

 sphere

Addition

Addition is adding one number to another.

two bears **plus three** bears **is five** bears

2 + 3 = 5

Capacity

A cup **holds less** than a bottle.

STUDENT GLOSSARY

Equals

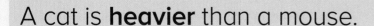

2 and 3 **balances** 5
2 and 3 **is equal to** 5
2 + 3 = 5

Equation

An **equation** has two parts and an equals symbol.
For example: 5 + 2 = 7, or 7 − 2 = 5

Mass

A cat is **heavier** than a mouse.

Number

Number tells how many in a group.

Numeral

A **numeral** is the symbol for a number.

Repeating patterns

The ☺☆ repeats in this pattern.

Subtraction

Subtraction is taking one number away from another.

five bears **take away two**
bears **is three** bears
5   −   2   =   3